High Beg.

STEPHEN COLBOURN

The Wall

D1178452

HEINEMANN ELT

Series Editor: John Milne

The Heinemann ELT Guided Readers provide a choice of enjoyable reading material for learners of English. The series is published at five levels – Starter, Beginner, Elementary, Intermediate and Upper. At **Beginner Level**, the control of content and language has the following main features:

Information Control
The stories are written in a fluent and pleasing style with straightforward plots and a restricted number of main characters. The cultural background is made explicit through both words and illustrations. Information which is vital to the story is clearly presented and repeated where necessary.

Structure Control
Special care is taken with sentence length. Most sentences contain only one clause, though compound sentences are used occasionally with the clauses joined by the conjunctions 'and', 'but', and 'or'. The use of these compound sentences gives the text balance and rhythm. The use of Past Simple and Past Continuous Tenses is permitted since these are the basic tenses used in narration and students must become familiar with these as they continue to extend and develop their reading ability.

Vocabulary Control
At **Beginner Level** there is a controlled vocabulary of approximately 600 basic words, so that students with a basic knowledge of English will be able to read with understanding and enjoyment. Help is also given in the form of vivid illustrations which are closely related to the text.

For further information on the full selection of Readers at all five levels in the series, please refer to the Heinemann ELT Readers catalogue.

Jarrad lived in a small village. His mother was dead. Jarrad lived with his father. His father was the village carpenter.

They lived in the land of Muraya. There was a huge wall in Muraya. The village was near the wall.

'What is the wall?' Jarrad asked his father.

'Nobody knows,' said his father. 'You cannot go round the wall. You cannot climb over the wall. You cannot see the other side of the wall.'

'What's on the other side of the wall?' asked Jarrad.

'Don't ask so many questions,' said his father.

One day in spring, Morpath came to the house. Morpath! Jarrad was afraid of Morpath. All the children were afraid of Morpath. Morpath was the Keeper of the Wall.

Morpath looked through the gate. He did not open the gate.

Jarrad was helping his father. They were cutting wood. Jarrad looked at the gate. He saw Morpath's long nose and small eyes. Morpath called to Jarrad's father.

'Jarrad will go to the wall tomorrow,' said Morpath.

4

'Do I have to go to the wall?' Jarrad asked his father.

'All the children go to the wall,' said his father. 'You will go to the wall tomorrow.'

Jarrad was unhappy. He did not sleep well that night. He had a dream about the wall.

In his dream, he stood in front of the wall. The wall was very high. There was a white mist in front of the wall. The white mist came closer and closer to Jarrad. He was afraid.

Jarrad woke up suddenly. It was morning. He remembered his dream. Then he remembered Morpath. He was unhappy. Today he must go to the wall with Morpath.

Morpath came to Jarrad's house in the middle of the morning. He stood outside the gate.

The children stood in front of the wall. It was dark and grey. Morpath pointed at the wall.

'Listen to me!' shouted Morpath. 'Wild people live on the other side of the wall. They have red eyes and sharp teeth. They are always hungry. The wall keeps us safe.'

The children were afraid. They looked up at the wall. The wall was very high.

'Can the wild people climb over the wall?' asked Jarrad.

'Silence!' shouted Morpath. 'Do not ask questions. The wild people will hear you. They will come and eat you. Do not go near the wall.'

'Have you seen the other side?' asked Jarrad. He was afraid.

'Did you hear me?' shouted Morpath. 'I told you – do not ask questions.'

Morpath walked up to Jarrad. 'Do you want to see the wild people?' he asked. 'Do you know what they like to eat? They like to eat children.'

Morpath looked at Jarrad. Jarrad looked at the ground.

Morpath looked at the other children. 'Remember,' he said, 'the wall is dangerous. The wild people are dangerous. Do not go near the wall. Do not ask questions!'

Suddenly, Morpath turned and looked at the wall.

'What's that?' he shouted. 'Look! There! Look at the top of the wall.'

The children looked. Jarrad looked. He could not see anything.

'The wild people are coming!' shouted Morpath. 'They are coming to eat you! *Run!*'

The children ran away. They ran back to the village. They were very frightened. Jarrad was frightened too. He ran with them, but he stopped near some bushes. He hid in the bushes and looked back.

Jarrad looked back at the wall. He did not see the wild people. But the wall was different. The wall was not dark and grey. Now it was bright and shining.

The children did not go near the wall again. They played together, but nobody went near the wall.

In summer, the children played a game. One child closed her eyes. She counted to ten very slowly. The other children hid behind rocks and trees. Then the child tried to find the other children.

Jarrad was playing the game. He hid in some thick bushes. He went down on his hands and knees. The bushes covered him completely.

Jarrad was a long way from the other children. Suddenly he looked up. There was a grey rock in front of him. But it was not a rock. It was the wall.

Jarrad was afraid. He did not want to go near the wall. He did not want to touch it. But he looked at the wall.

At first, it was dark and grey. Then the wall changed. Now it was bright and shining. The bright light hurt Jarrad's eyes.

Then Jarrad saw a boy. But he could not see the boy's face. Who was this boy?

Jarrad put his hands over his eyes. Was he dreaming? The boy's hands were over the boy's eyes! Was the wall a mirror? Jarrad was frightened.

Jarrad forgot the children's game. He ran home and told his father.

Jarrad was surprised. His father did not believe him.

'Don't be silly,' his father said. 'Don't tell stupid stories. And don't play near the wall. Morpath will be angry.'

Jarrad ran back to the wall and looked at it. But now the wall was not bright and shining. It was dark and grey.

'Come away from there!' shouted a child. 'What are you doing?'

'I'm looking through the wall,' said Jarrad.

Jarrad's friends laughed at him. 'What can you see?' shouted one child. 'What can you see on the other side? Can you see the wild people?'

'We're going to tell Morpath about you,' shouted another child. 'Morpath will be angry.'

Jarrad walked home slowly. His friends were laughing at him. Nobody believed him.

Morpath was angry. He came to see Jarrad's father. Jarrad listened. Morpath shouted angrily at Jarrad.

That night, Jarrad dreamt about the wall again. Jarrad saw the wild people. They had red eyes and sharp teeth. They were hungry. They were trying to climb the wall.

Jarrad had many bad dreams. He became ill. Jarrad's father was very worried.

An old man lived outside the village. People called him the Wise Man. Jarrad's father went and spoke to the Wise Man.

'My son is ill,' he said. 'The wall has made him ill. Morpath has made him ill. What must I do?'

'I will come to your son,' said the Wise Man. 'But do not tell Morpath. Morpath does not like me.'

The Wise Man came to see Jarrad at night. Jarrad was in bed. Jarrad was ill. He was very hot. He said the same words again and again.

'They're coming to eat me,' Jarrad said. 'They're coming to eat me.'

'Who is coming to eat you?' the Wise Man asked.

'The wild people,' said Jarrad. 'They're coming over the wall. They have red eyes and sharp teeth. They are always hungry.'

'I know these people,' the Wise Man said.

Jarrad sat up in bed. 'How do you know them?' he asked.

'I dream about them too,' replied the Wise Man.

'Have you seen them?' asked Jarrad. 'Have you seen their red eyes and sharp teeth?'

'No,' replied the Wise Man. 'In my dreams they haven't got red eyes and sharp teeth. In my dreams they all look like you and me.'

'Do they want to eat us?' asked Jarrad.

'No,' said the Wise Man. 'They don't want to eat us. They are happy with the wall. They are afraid of us. The wall keeps *us* out. The wall keeps *them* safe.'

'Are they afraid of us?' asked Jarrad.

'Yes,' said the Wise Man. 'They have never seen us. And so, they are afraid of us. We have never seen them. And so, we are afraid of them.'

Jarrad closed his eyes. He wanted to sleep.

'Sleep now,' said the Wise Man. 'You will not have bad dreams.'

The next day, Jarrad felt much better. He went to look at the wall. He was not afraid of the wall any more.

'One day,' Jarrad said, 'I will find out all about the wall. Who built the wall? Why did they build it? What is on the other side of the wall? How can I get over the wall? How can I see the other side? One day, I will find out the answers to these questions.'

Many years passed. Jarrad grew up. He often thought about the wall. He had looked through the wall. He had seen the boy on the other side. He often dreamt about the other side of the wall. But these dreams were not bad dreams.

Jarrad did not talk about the wall to anybody. He was afraid of Morpath. Everybody was afraid of Morpath, the Keeper of the Wall.

Jarrad worked with his father. He learned to be a carpenter. There was no school in the village. His father taught him everything.

Jarrad learned to measure with a stick and string. He

16

learned to make tables, stools and benches. Then he learned to build houses.

All the houses in the village were long and low. They had one or two windows. The walls were made of wood and mud. The roofs were made of straw. There were holes in the roofs. The smoke from the fires went out of the holes. Rain came through the holes. The floors were wet and muddy.

The houses were close together. Sometimes a fire started in one house. Then the fire spread to other houses. Sometimes many houses caught fire and burned down.

Jarrad was now twenty years old.

It was summer and the weather was hot. The roofs of the houses were dry. Sparks from a cooking fire set one roof on fire. The fire spread to the next house, then the next. Soon, the whole street was burning.

Everybody was shouting, 'Fire! Fire!' They were all running to the river. They carried water in buckets from the river.

Jarrad and his father could not save their house. The roof caught fire. Soon the walls were burning. Jarrad and his father pulled tables and chairs out into the street. They saved many things. But the house burned down.

By evening, all the houses were black and burnt. Black smoke covered the village. The village people slept beside the river.

'We will be busy,' said Jarrad's father. 'All the houses must be built again.'

'But we must build them in a different way,' said Jarrad. 'The houses are too close together. We must build them further apart.'

'We can't,' said his father. 'The land beside the river is bad. We can't build near the river. And we can't build near the wall. We must build in the old way. We must build the houses in the same place.'

That night, Jarrad had a dream. He saw the other side of the wall. There was a fire. He carried water from the river. He smelt the black smoke and saw the orange flames. The village was burning.

Then, in his dream, he built a new house. He built the house in a different way. It was a different kind of house. It was not close to the other houses.

Jarrad woke up. He had an idea. That morning, he told his father. He told his friends.

'In the past we always built long, low houses,' said Jarrad. 'But I want to build a tall, thin house. We can have a room on the ground. And we can put a room on top. Then there will be more space between the houses.'

'But nobody has done that before,' said his father.

'I'll show you,' said Jarrad. 'Let's try.'

Jarrad's friends helped him. He showed them how to build the new house. It had two floors. There was a ladder between the floors. The roof did not have a hole in the middle. The cooking fire was in a small kitchen. There was a chimney over the cooking fire. The chimney was built through the roof. The smoke went up the chimney.

After two weeks, they finished the house. Everybody came to look at it. It was different. It was new.

Morpath came to look at the new house. Morpath was not pleased.

'New things are bad,' he said. 'New ideas are bad. This house is bad.'

But the village people were happy. They told people in other villages. Soon everybody in Muraya heard about the new house.

The news went to the capital city. The King of Muraya heard the news.

The King sent a messenger to Jarrad. The messenger asked, 'How high can you build?'

Jarrad said, 'Let me think. I will give you my answer tomorrow.'

That night, Jarrad had a dream. He saw the other side of the wall. People were building a tall house. The messenger came to the tall house. He asked Jarrad, 'How high can you build?'

In his dream, Jarrad replied, 'I can build as high as the wall.'

Jarrad woke up and went to the King's messenger.

'I can build as high as the wall,' he said.

After two weeks, the messenger came again.

'The King is coming to your village,' the messenger told Jarrad. 'He is coming to your village in two months' time. In two months you must build as high as the wall.'

Jarrad needed the help of many men. All the young men wanted to help.

But Morpath did not like the idea.

'New things are bad things,' said Morpath. 'Do not make

new things. Do not ask questions. Do not go near the wall.'

But a messenger came from the King. The messenger said, 'Help Jarrad to build as high as the wall.'

Two months later, the King came to the village. He came with his horses and soldiers.

Have you built a house as high as the wall?

No, your Majesty. I have not.

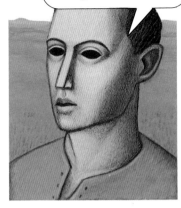

25

The King followed Jarrad. They went outside the village. They went to the wall.

Jarrad had built nine platforms. The platforms were on top of each other. The top platform was near the top of the wall. Workmen were finishing the top platform.

'See, Your Majesty,' said Jarrad, 'I have built as high as the wall. I am going to climb to the top of the wall. I will be the first person to look over the wall.'

Morpath came up to the King. He was angry. 'We must not look over the wall,' he said. 'There are wild people on the other side. They will climb the wall. They will kill us all. We must burn these platforms.'

'But I want to know,' said the King. 'We must know. Are there people on the other side or not? Jarrad, go and look.'

Jarrad carried a short ladder. He went to the platforms. He climbed onto the first, then onto the second. He climbed to the top platform. Then he put his ladder against the top of the wall. He climbed to the top of the dark, grey wall.

The King watched. The King's soldiers watched. The villagers watched. Morpath watched.

They saw Jarrad at the top of the wall. Then they saw something moving. A head appeared on the other side of the wall. Somebody was climbing up from the other side!

'Run!' shouted Morpath. 'The wild people are coming. They will eat us all!'

Everybody started to run. They ran away from the wall. But the King did not run. He stood looking at the wall.

Jarrad was not frightened. He saw a face on the other side of the wall. It was the face of a man. Jarrad knew the man.

'I've seen you in my dreams,' said Jarrad. 'I've seen you on the other side of the wall.'

'And I have seen *you*,' the other man said.

Jarrad looked over the wall. There was a village on the other side. It was like his own village. And there was a river near the village.

There were many people near the wall. Jarrad looked at them. They started to run. They ran away from the wall.

Jarrad looked at the other man. The man was standing on a platform. It was like Jarrad's platform.

'Will you come down my side?' Jarrad asked. 'Or shall I come down yours?'

'I'll come down your side,' said the man. He came over

to Jarrad's side of the wall. They climbed down the platforms together.

Suddenly, the wall changed. It was not dark and grey. It was bright and shining. Then it became clear as glass. Jarrad saw through the wall.

They walked up to the King of Muraya. The King stood alone. All the others had run away.

Suddenly, they heard a sound. They heard the sound of crashing wood. The platforms had fallen down.

'Look!' said the King. 'The wall has disappeared!'

Macmillan Heinemann English Language Teaching, Oxford

A division of Macmillan Publishers Limited

Companies and representatives throughout the world

ISBN 0 435 27181 4

Heinemann is a registered trade mark of Reed Educational and Professional Publishing Limited

© Stephen Colbourn 1993
First published 1993

Illustrated by Simon Noyes
Typography by Threefold Design
Cover by Symon Noyes and Threefold Design
Typeset in 12/16pt Goudy
Printed and bound in Malta by Interprint Limited

2003   2002   2001   2000   1999
    12   11   10   9   8   7   6